G R A P H I S T O C K

C A T A L O G   4

G R A P H I S T O C K

C A T A L O G 4

TELEPHONE
1-800-4-IMAGES or 212-849-2900

FACSIMILE
212-691-6609

INTERNET
www.images.com

GRAPHISTOCK, INC. A DIVISION OF IMAGES.COM, INC. 16 WEST 19TH STREET, NEW YORK NY 10011
STOCK ILLUSTRATION SOURCE—SPOTS ON THE SPOT—SIS NOSTALGIA—GRAPHISTOCK

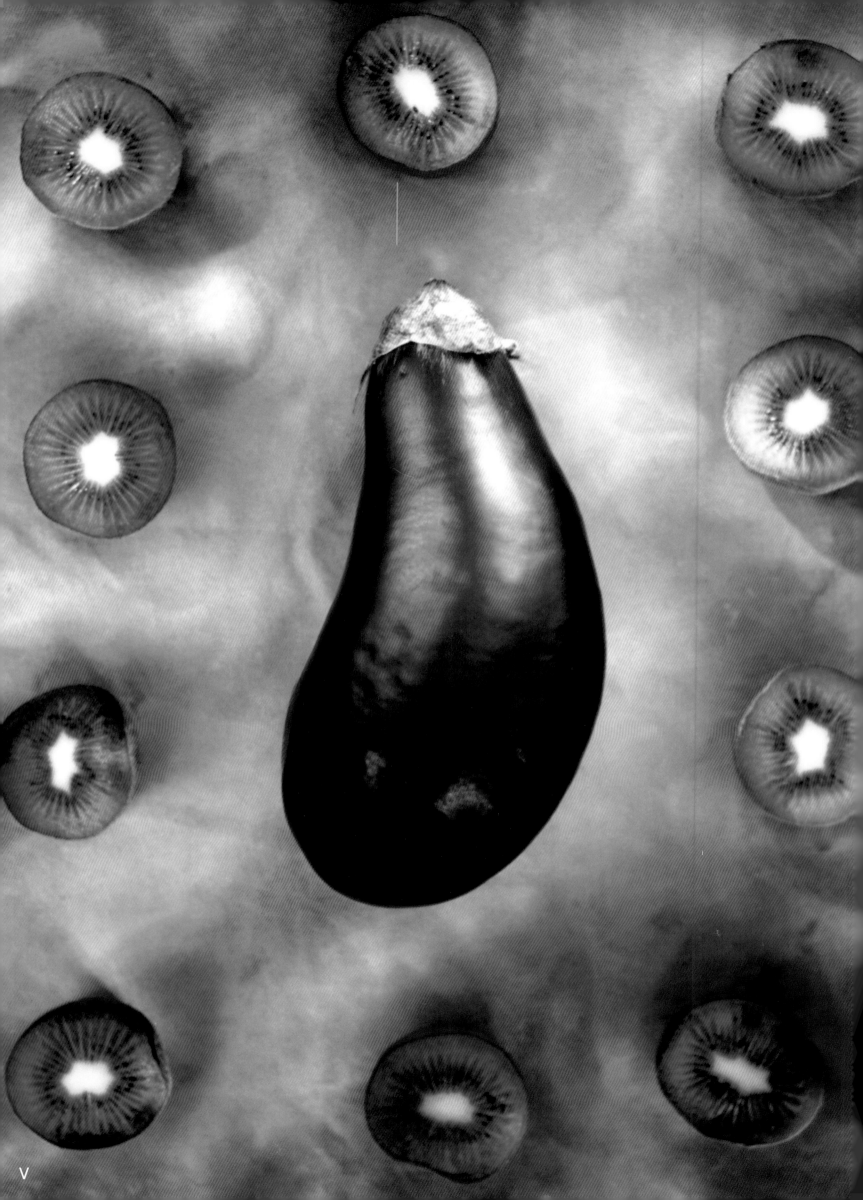

STAFF

PUBLISHED BY GRAPHISTOCK, A DIVISION OF IMAGES.COM, INC. CREATIVE DIRECTOR CARRE BEVILACQUA SALES DIRECTOR MARIE BOUVET SALES LISE SEGUIN, ANDREA MORETTI RESEARCH MANAGER CATHERINE EDKINS RESEARCHERS ERIKA IZQUIERDO, REBECCA FLOYD.

HOW TO USE

GRAPHISTOCK CATALOG 4 IS ARRANGED BY PHOTOGRAPHER. TO SEARCH BY SUBJECT MATTER PLEASE REFER TO THE INDEX AT THE BACK OF THE CATALOG. ONCE YOU'VE LOCATED THE IMAGES YOU'D LIKE TO CONSIDER, SIMPLY CALL US AND GIVE US THEIR IDENTIFYING NUMBERS. IF YOU DON'T FIND EXACTLY THE IMAGE YOU'RE LOOKING FOR, GIVE US YOUR IDEAS OR A SPECIFIC DESCRIPTION OR FAX US YOUR LAYOUT — WE MAY HAVE THE IMAGE YOU NEED IN OUR FILES. ALTERNATIVELY, YOU CAN QUICKLY ACCESS EVERY IMAGE IN OUR FILES ON OUR INTERNET SITE AT www.images.com. GRAPHISTOCK CHARGES A NOMINAL RESEARCH FEE FOR MANUAL SEARCHES BUT THIS FEE IS WAIVED IF YOU DECIDE TO PURCHASE REPRODUCTION RIGHTS TO AN IMAGE. ALL ORDERS ARE FILLED THE SAME DAY WE RECEIVE THEM. IN NEW YORK CITY WE OFFER SAME DAY MESSENGER DELIVERY AND OVERNIGHT DELIVERY ANYWHERE IN THE UNITED STATES. IN ADDITION, DRUM-SCANNED OR DIGITAL VERSIONS OF THE IMAGES MAY BE DOWNLOADED WITHIN MINUTES FROM OUR FTP SITE.

USING THE GRAPHISTOCK WEB SITE

1.TYPE www.images.com IN YOUR BROWSER (THEN REGISTER IF YOU HAVEN'T USED THE SITE BEFORE) 2. CLICK ON THE GRAPHISTOCK BUTTON 3. CLICK ON "KEYWORD" OR "PHOTOGRAPHERS NAME" SEARCH BUTTON 4. TYPE IN THE APPROPRIATE KEYWORDS OR SELECT PHOTOGRAPHER'S NAME 5. REVIEW YOUR SELECTION (IMAGES MAY BE DOWNLOADED FOR ROUGH LAYOUTS).

ADDITIONAL SERVICES

ANY GRAPHISTOCK IMAGE CAN BE PROVIDED AS A HIGH-RESOLUTION DRUM SCAN.

CREDITS

COVER CHRISTOPHER WRAY-McCANN I ROGER CAMP II GWEN AKIN III JERALD FRAMPTON IV TELEPHONE: JEREMY WOLFF FACSIMILE: LEIGH BEISCH INTERNET: JOHN WEBER V LESLIE KAHL VI JOHN WEBER VII TINA WEST VIII TOM FRANCISCO BACK COVER PAUL McGUIRK PHOTOGRAPHER'S INDEX LEIGH BEISCH SUBJECT INDEX JANET BELLER INSIDE BACK COVER HOWARD SCHATZ

PORTFOLIOS

G1501-26

G1501-111

G1501-31

G1501-150

G1501-118

G1501-23

G1501-107

G1501-149

G1501-153

G1501-133

G1502-58

G1502-56

G1502-72

G1502-83

G1502-25

G1502-27

G1504-10

G1504-08

G1504-05

G1504-06

G1504-02

G1504-01

G1504-07

G1504-04

G1504-13

G1504-12

G1504-14

G1504-09

G1504-11

G1504-03

G1622-20

G1622-02

G1622-55

G1622-33

G1622-49

G1622-61

G1622-60

G1622-26

G1622-57

G1622-63

G1622-54

G1622-32

G1622-46

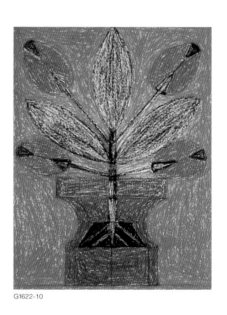

G1622-10

G1622-11

G1622-53

G1622-30

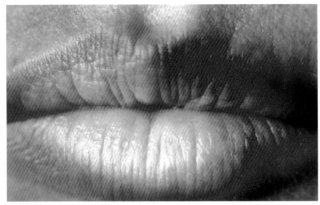

G1507-693

G1507-666

G1507-642

G1507-81

G1507-735

G1507-421

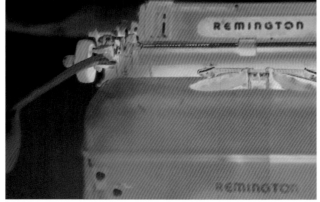

G1507-555

G1507-556

G1507-709

G1507-707

G1507-723

G1507-415

G1507-12

G1507-110

G1507-746

G1507-749

G1507-521

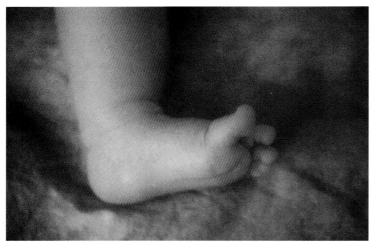

G1509-34

G1509-148

G1509-134

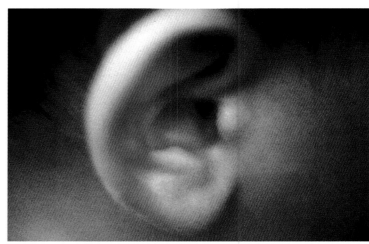

G1509-35

G1509-157

G1509-100

G1509-47

G1509-13

G1509-66

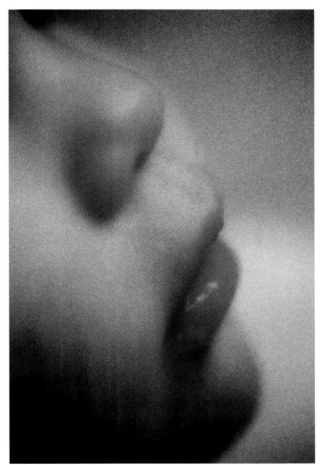

G1509-32

G1510-264

G1510-154

G1510-225

G1510-160

G1510-278

G1510-247

G1510-191

G1510-57

G1510-262

G1510-13

G1510-121

G1510-208

G1510-186

G1510-232

G1510-21

G1510-207

G1510-197

G1511-125

G1511-99

G1511-248

G1511-178

G1511-210

G1566-419

G1566-753

G1566-371

G1566-218

G1566-592

G1566-385

G1566-372

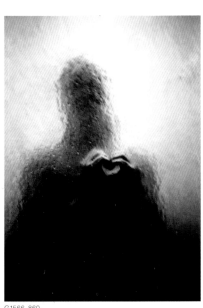

G1566-860

G1566-744

G1566-16

G1566-481

G1566-546

G1566-652

G1566-614

G1566-199

G1566-464

G1566-1021

G1514-277

G1514-168

G1514-341

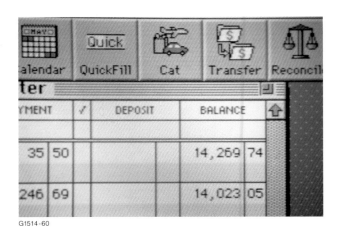

G1514-60

G1514-89

G1514-81

G1514-82

G1514-201

G1514-340

G1514-196

G1514-344

G1514-187

G1514-243

G1514-233

G1514-205

G1514-198

G1514-245

G1515-148

G1515-102

G1515-207

G1515-216

G1515-165

G1515-215

G1515-124

G1515-164

G1515-107

G1515-42

G1515-86

G1515-130

G1515-151

G1515-92

G1515-136

G1515-188

G1515-48

G1516-05

G1516-19

G1516-20

G1516-24

G1516-04

G1516-21

G1516-23

G1516-09

G1516-25

G1516-26

G1516-17

G1516-28

-4-IMAGES

G1518-08

G1518-02

G1518-32

G1518-14

G1518-33

G1518-17

G1518-34

G1518-35

G1518-20

G1518-36

G1518-03

G1513-06

G1513-04

G1513-02

G1513-01

G1513-07

G1513-05

G1513-03

G1520-20

G1520-19

G1520-18

G1520-31

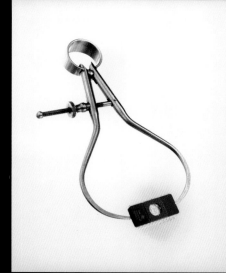

G1520-60

G1520-38

G1520-45

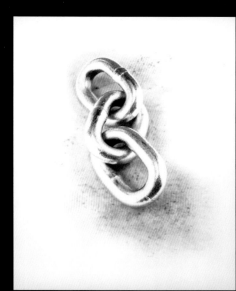

G1520-34

G1520-10

G1520-63

G1520-61

G1665-12

G1665-17

G1665-05

G1665-15

G1665-03

G1665-11

G1665-19

G1665-09

G1665-20

G1665-13

G1665-06

G1€65-02

G1665-16

G1665-04

G1665-18

G1665-14

G1665-10

G1665-07

G1665-01

G1665-08

G1522-05

G1522-06

G1522-01

G1522-07

G1522-02

G1522-04

G1522-03

G1522-08

G1531-01

G1531-02

G1531-03

G1531-06

G1531-07

G1531-04

G1531-05

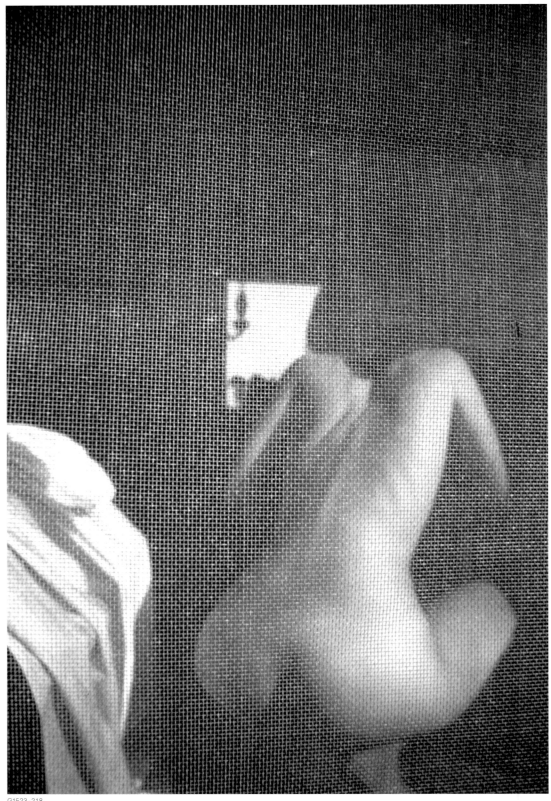

G1523-218

G1523-48

G1523-49

G1523-50

G1523-51

G1523-52

G1523-56

G1523-57

G1523-72

G1523-59

G1524-101

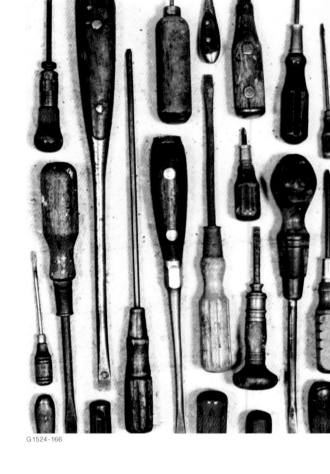

G1524-166

G1524-149

G1524-227

G1524-258

G1525 - 09

G1525 - 07

G1525 - 08

G1525 - 11

G1525-10

G1525-04

G1525-05

G1525-03

G1525-02

G1525-06

G1526-13

G1526-40

G1526-12

G1526-41

G1526-32

G1526-48

G1526-33

G1526-47

G1526-39

G1526-31

G1526-29

G1526-14

G1527-77

G1527-35

G1527-52

G1527-51

G1527-23

G1528-131

G1528-134

G1528-213

G1528-120

G1528-132

G1528-22

G1528-48

G1528-180

G1528 - 185

G1532-14

G1532-55

G1532-66

G1532-38

G1532-47

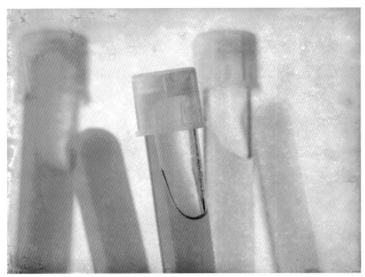

81533-47

81533-01

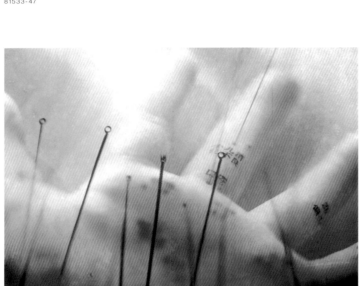

81533-85

81533-48

81533-41

81533-46

81533-63

81533-62

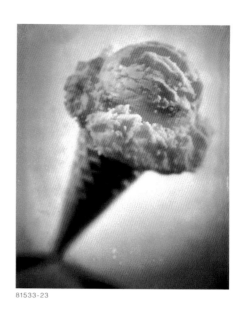

81533-23

81533-56

81533-52

81533-42

81533-79

81533-50

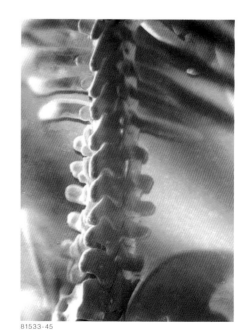

81533-45

G1535-333

G1535-332

G1535-175

G1535-189

G1535-56

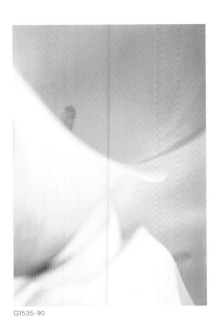

G1535-90

G1535-220

G1535-249

G1535-125

G1535-55

G1535-22

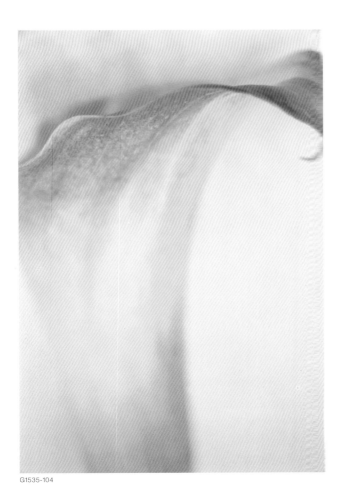

G1535-104

G1535-81

G1536-185

G1536-108

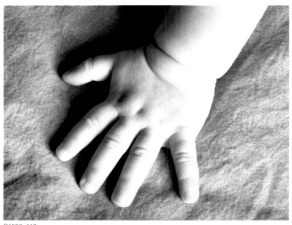

G1536-112

G1536-206

G1536-106

G1536-275

G1536-289

G1536-49

G1536-01

G1536-91

G1536-165

G1536-167

G1536-241

G1536-312

G1536-05

G1536-131

G1622-40

G1622-41

G1622-42

G1622-44

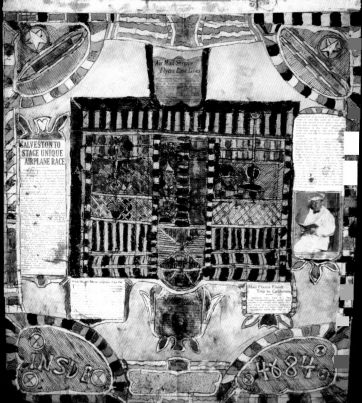

G1622-58

G1622-39

G1622-50

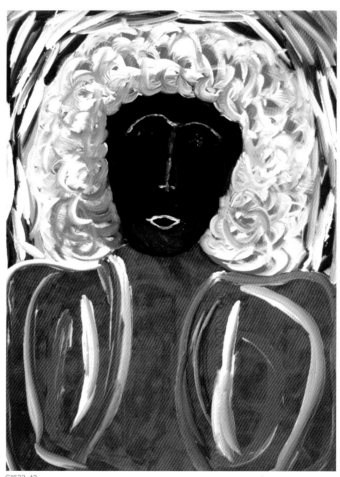

G1622-43

G1622-15

G1622-51

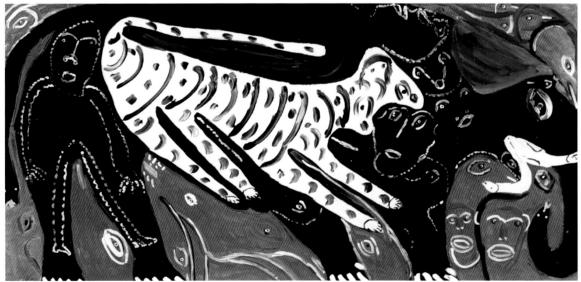

G1622-59

G1537-33

G1537-27

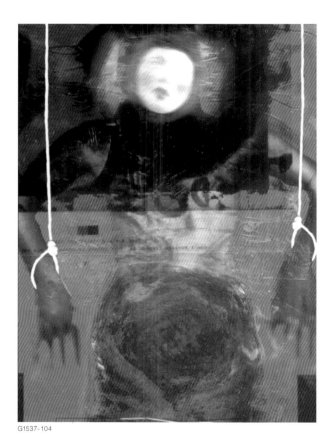

G1537-104

G1537-51

G1537-44

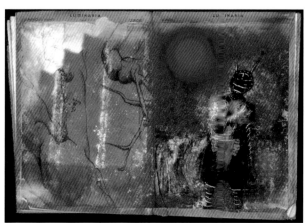

G1537-70

G1537-46

G1537-50

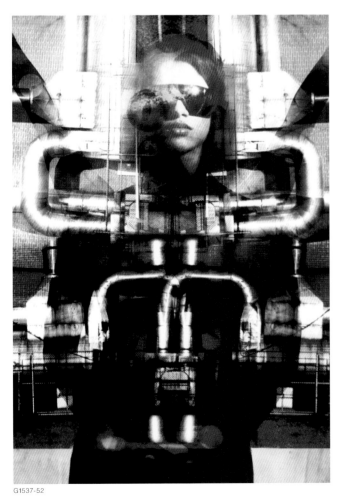

G1537-52

G1537-67

G1540-298

G1540-51

G1540-91

G1540-108

G1540-314

G1540-443

G1540-220

G1540-316

G1540-168

G1540-392

G1540-341

G1540-231

G1541-178

G1541-49

G1541-99

G1541-101

G1541-88

G1541-114

G1541-109

G1541-87

G1541-95

G1541-45

G1541-113

G1541-115

G1541-94

G1541-111

G1541-89

G1541-91

G1542-32

G1542-09

G1542-36

G1542-12

G1542-02

G1542-13

G1544-195

G1609-19

G1609-91

G1609-90

G1609-59

G1609-47

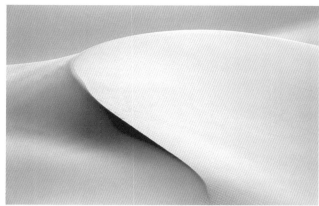

G1609-17

G1609-53

G1609-22

G1609-68

G1609-67

G1609-13

G1609-66

G1609-03

G1545-06

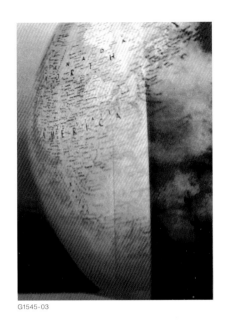

G1545-03

G1545-04

G1545-02

G1545-10

G1545-01

G1545-05

G1545-09

G1545-08

G1545-07

G1546-03

G1546-10

G1546-15

G1546-47

G1546-58

G1546-08

G1546-09

G1546-48

G1546-11

G1546-74

G1546-68

G1546-02

G1547-38

G1547-05

G1547-47

G1547-130

G1547-46

G1547-62

G1547-146

G1547-42

G1547-64

G1547-31

G1547-63

G1547-19

G1547-08

G1547-151

G1547-44

G1547-114

G1547-89

G1548-130

G1548-153

G1548-85

G1548-121

G1548-79

G1548-98

G1548-11

G1548-62

G1548-148

G1548-170

G1548-159

G1548-33

G1548-28

G1548-165

G1548-207

G1548-146

G1548-78

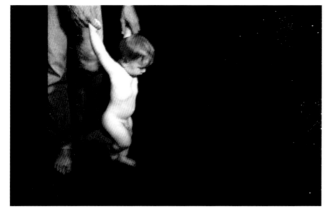

G1552-09

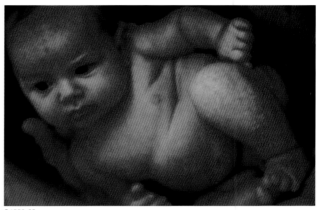

G1552-55

G1552-38

G1552-43

G1552-51

G1552-59

G1552-10

G1552-15

G1552-82

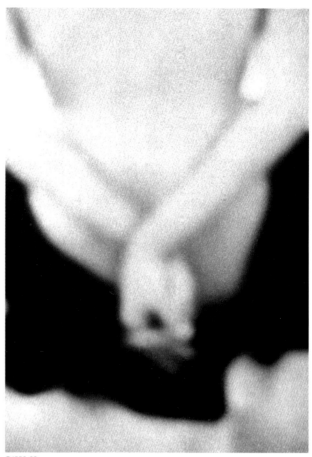

G1552-83

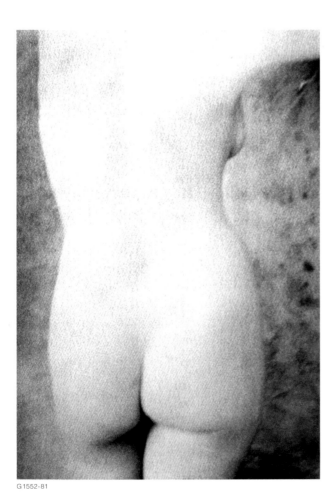

G1552-81

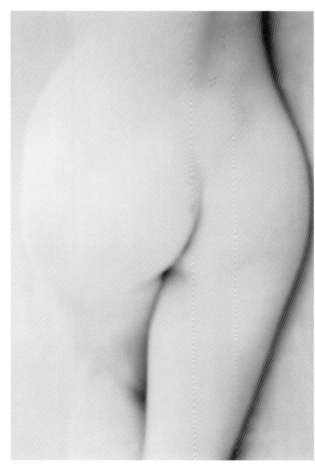

G1552-89

G1549-09

G1549-08

G1549-13

G1549-04

G1549-12

G1549-25

G1549-20

G1549-26

G1549-33

G1549-06

G1549-37

G1549-11

G1549-38

G1549-32

G1549-43

G1549-28

G1549-19

G1549-14

G1551-11

G1551-29

G1550-05

G1550-25

G1550-27

G1550-04

G1503-98

G1503-273

G1503-118

G1503-107

G1503-366

G15C3-238

G1622-47

G1622-12

G1622-29

G1622-62

G1622-45

G1622-08

G1622-16

G1622-03

G1553-43

G1553-28

G1553-06

G1553-30

G1553-31

G1553-21

G1553-32

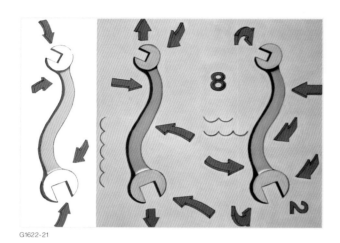

G1622-21

G1622-13

G1622-09

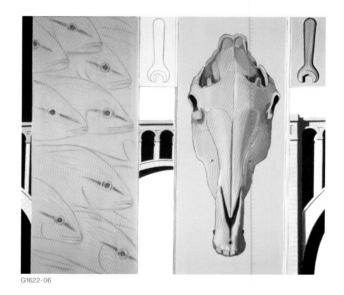

G1622-06

G1622-07

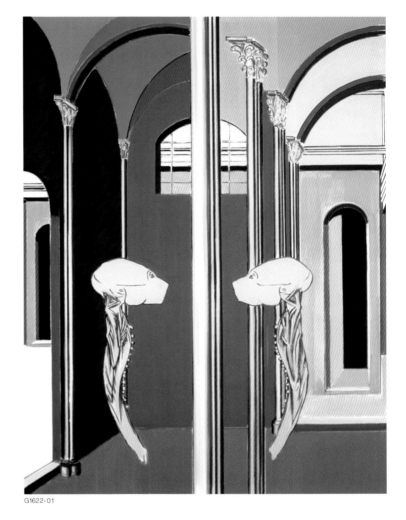

G1622-01

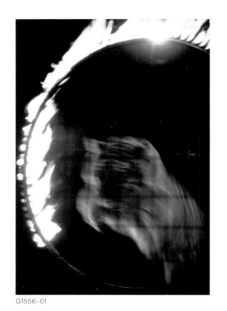

G1556-01

G1556-02

G1556-03

G1556-04

G1556-05

G1556-06

G1556-07

G1556-08

G1556-09

G1556-10

G1556-13

G1556-11

G1556-12

G1558-147

G1558-149

G1558-144

G1558-140

G1558-138

G1558-146

G1558-139

G1558-136

G1558-141

G1558-142

G1558-145

G1558-150

G1558-143

G1558-137

G1558-148

G1560-14

G1560-73

G1-60-139

G1561-03

G1561-07

G1561-09

G1561-10

G1561-16

G1561-15

G1561-06

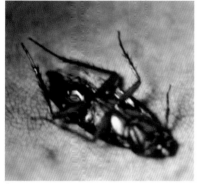

G1561-01

G1561-02

G1561-11

31561-12

G1561-13

G1561-14

G1561-04

G1561-08

G1561-05

G1562-199

G1562-04

G1562-87

G1562-86

G1562-21

G1562-66

G1562-109

G1562-75

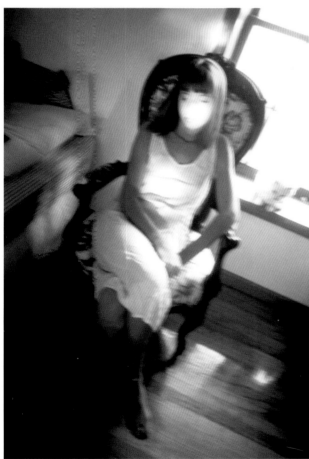

G1562-180

G1562-100

G1666-11

G1666-02

G1666-03

G1666-05

G1666-01

G1666-04

G1666-09

G1666-10

G1666-08

G1666-06

G1666-07

G1622-25

G1622-18

G1622-24

G1622-05

G1622-22

G1622-14

G1622-04

G1622-31

G1622-56

G1622-65

G1565-01

G1565-05

G1565-138

G1565-29

G1565-127

G1565-184

G1565-54

G1565-61

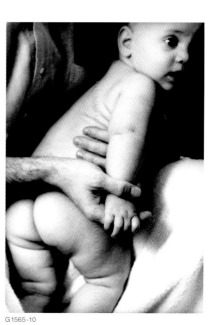

G1565-10

G1565-39

G1565-65

G1565-190

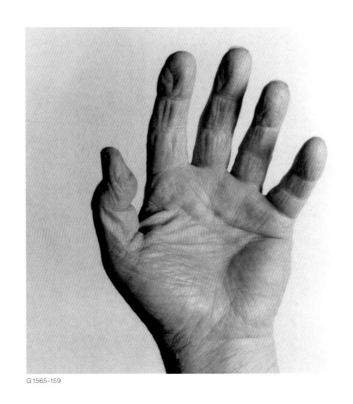

G1565-159

G1565-92

G1565-171

G1569-170

G1569-58

G1569-01

G1569-15

G1569-230

G1569-62

G1569-209

G1569-66

G1569-51

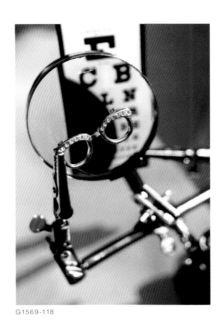

G1569-118

G1569-13

G1569-127

G1569-37

G1569-90

G1569-50

G1569-80

G1569-164

G1572-10

G1572-47

G1572-60

G1572-33

G1572-03

G1572-51

G1572-02

G1572-17

G1572-38

G1573-90

G1573-162

G1573-136

G1573-27

G1573-145

G1573-116

G1573-147

G1573-146

G1573-102

G1573-61

G1573-130

G1573-79

G1573-149

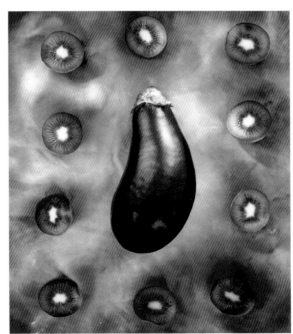

G1573-177

G1576-02

G1576-45

G1576-19

G1576-31

G1577-14

G1577-71

G1577-44

G1577-81

G1577-13

G1577-62

G1577-33

G1577-03

G1577-77

G1578-51

G1578-29

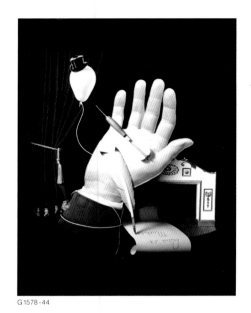

G1578-44

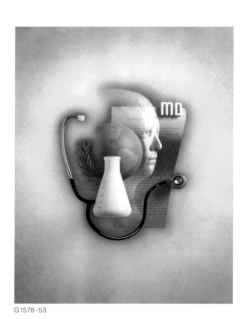

G1578-53

G1578-26

G1578-27

G1578-15

G1578-14

G1578-34

G1578-42

G1586-09

G1586-22

G1586-05

G1586-19

G1586-32

G1586-37

G1586-02

G1586-29

G1586-07

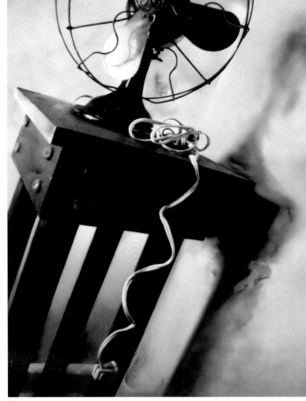

G1586-01

G1580-23

G1580-24

G1580-27

G1580-26

G1580-21

G1580-22

G1580-25

G1581-22

G1581-55

G1581-49

G1581-151

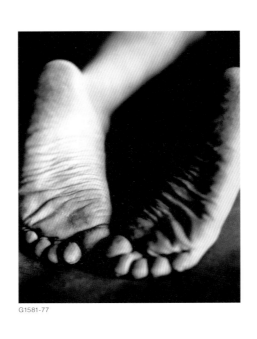

G1581-77

G1581-150

G1581-114

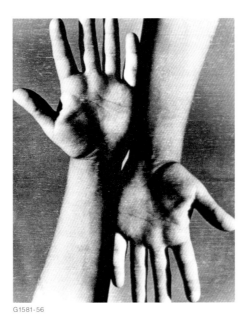

G1581-56

G1581-105

G1581-82

G1581-44

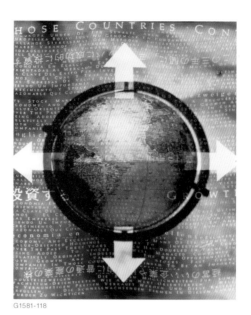

G1581-118

G1581-54

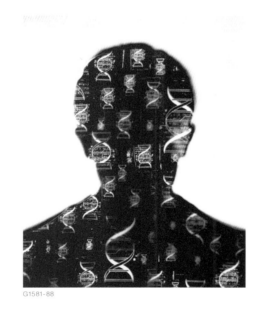

G1581-88

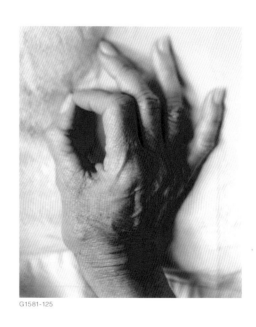

G1581-125

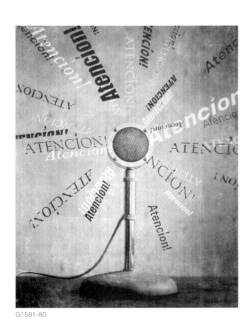

G1581-80

G1581-103

G1581-81

G1582-43

G1582-14

G1582-42

G1582-28

G1582-32

G1532-44

G1582-45

G1582-04

G1582-03

G1582-07

G1582-17

G1582-12

G153-28

G1583-04

G153-61

G1583-47

G153-24

G1583-02

G1583-68

G1583-36

G1583-58

G1583-50

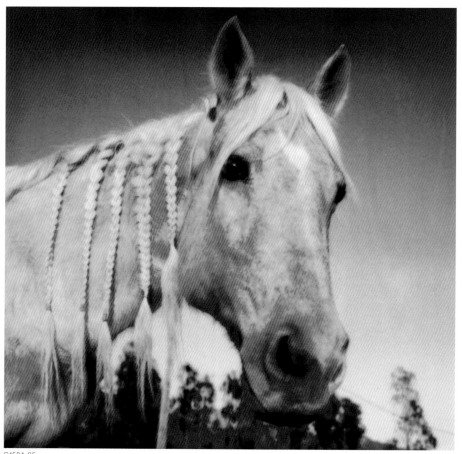

G1584-05

G1584-10

G1584-01

G1584-11

G1584-06

G1584-12

G1584-08

G1584-03

G1584-07

G1584-04

G1584-09

G1584-13

G1584-02

G1585-08

G1585-35

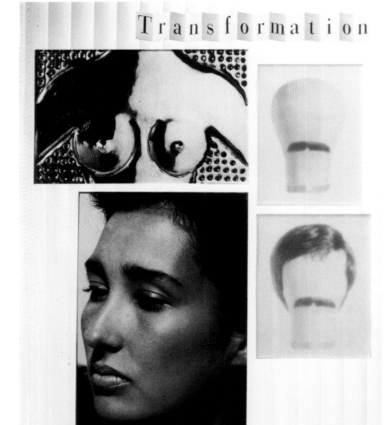

Transformation

G1585-28

G1585-17

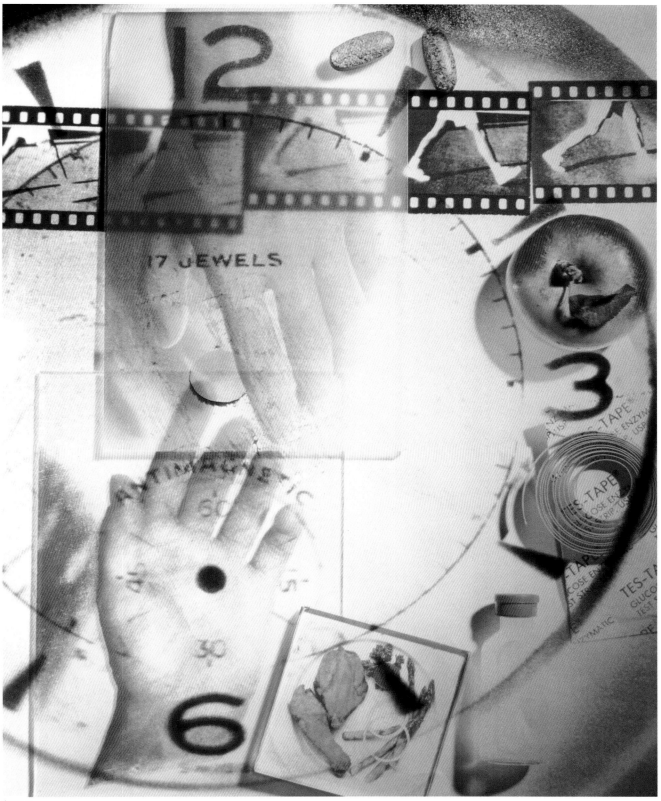

G1585-62

G1587-219

G1587-227	G1587-70	G1587-231
G1587-225	G1587-229	G1587-213
G1587-220	G1587-238	G1587-232
G1587-214	G1587-217	G1587-224

G1587-216

G1587-212	G1587-226	G1587-237
G1587-233	G1587-215	G1587-222
G1587-218	G1587-236	G1587-234
G1587-235	G1587-223	G1587-230

G1588-01

G1588-08

G1588-13

G1588-11

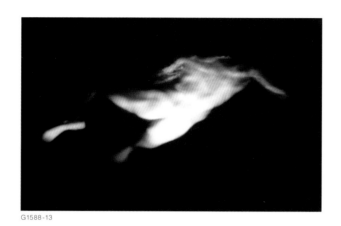

G1588-10

G1588-11

G1588-10

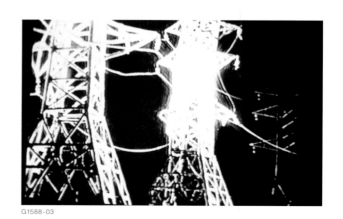

G1588-03

G1583-16

G1588-07

G1588-12

G1588-05

G1588-04

G1588-09

G1588-14

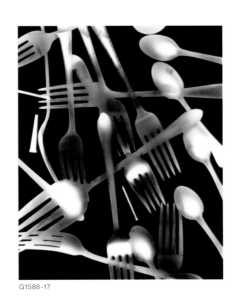

G1588-17

G1588-15

G1590-02

G1590-04

G1590-12

G1590-01

G1590-11

G1590-13

G1590-09

G1590-10

G1590-05

G1590-07

G1590-08

G1590-06

G1590-03

G1592-31

G1592-139

G1592-138

G1592-152

G1592-140

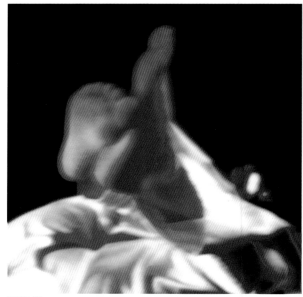

G1592-229

G1592-32

G1592-54

G1592-79

G1592-21

G1592-15

G1592-276

G1592-99

G1592-98

G1660-08

G1660-11

G1660-04

G1660-07

G1660-06

G1660-03

G1660-10

G1660-02

G1660-09

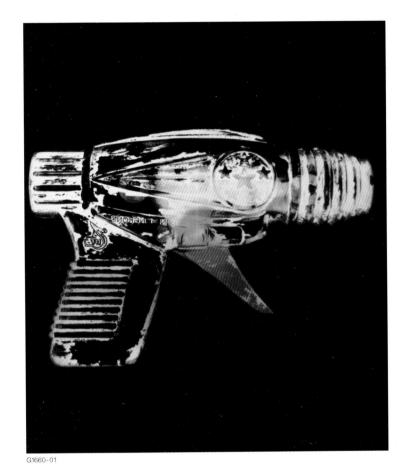

G1660-01

G1660-05

G1594-33

G1594-39

G1594-21

G1594-26

G1594-22

G1594-58

G1594-06

G1595-06

G1595-04

G1595-02

G1595-01

G1595-03

G1595-05

G1596-123

G1596-120

G1596-122

G1596-119

G1596-127

G1596-129

G1596-126

G1596-125

G1596-124

G1596-128

G1596-118

G1596-121

G1599-118

G1599-93

G1599-100

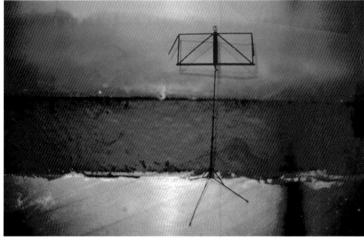

G1599-85

G1599-62

G1599-107

G1599-54

G1599-104

G1599-37

G1599-57

G1599-103

G1599-75

G1599-23

G1599-98

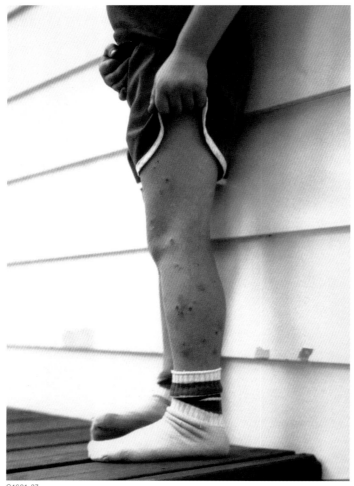

G1601-37

G1601-77

G1601-116

G1601-121

G1601-149

G1601-94

G1601-50

G1601-03

G1601-29

G1601-39

G1601-33

G1601-203

G1602-61

G1602-62

G1602-145

G1602-36

G1602-49

G1602-17

G1602-28

G1602-10

G1602-93

G1602-160

G1603-04

G1603-06

G1604-467

G1604-457

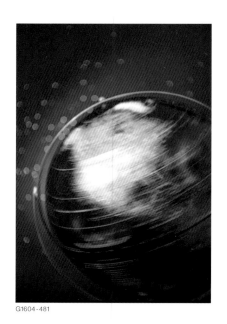

G1604-481

G1604-452

G1604-451

G1604-459

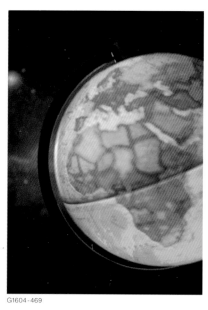

G1604-469

G1604-460

G1604-464

G1604-458

G1604-477

G1604-453

G1604-456

G1604-465

G1604-478

G1604-473

G1604-479

G1605-73

G1605-82

G1605-113

G1605-40

G1605-80

G1605-120

G1605-69

G1605-01

G1605-72

G1605-32

G1605-03

G1605-45

G1605-70

G1605-50

G1605-81

G1605-119

G1606-224

G1606-223

G1606-158

G1606-156

G1606-160

G1606-155

G1606-139

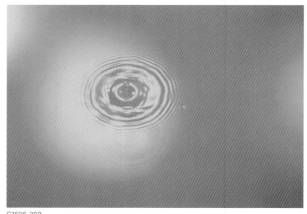

G1606-202

G1606-166

G1606-218

G1606 12

G1606-219

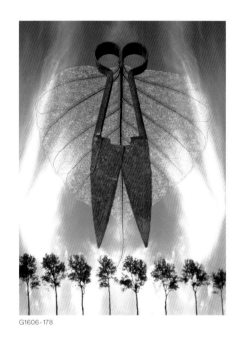

G1606-178

G1606- 25

G1606-222

G1606-220

G1606-21

G1609-41

G1609-40

G1609-39

G1538-269

G1538-266

G1538-262

G1538-268

G1538-276

G1538-267

G1538-273

G1538-270

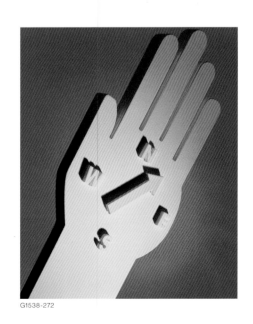

G1538-272

G1538-275

G1538-264

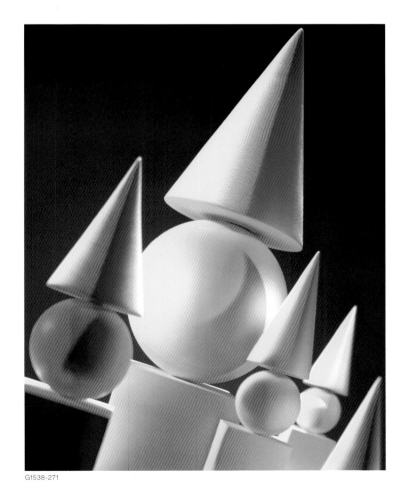

G1538-271

G1538-274

G1610-108

G1610-112

G1610-107

G1610-111

G1610-113

G1610-110

G1610-109

G1612-27

G1612-72

G1612-25

G1612-84

G1612-91

G1612-105

G1612-10

G1612-85

G1612-13

G1612-04

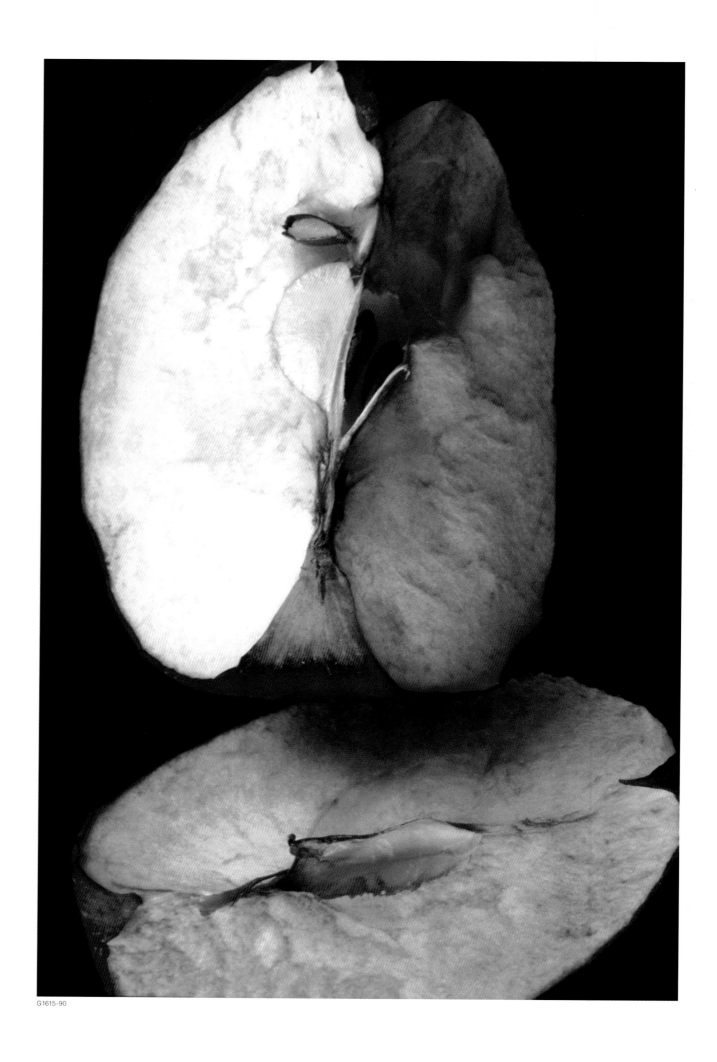

G1615-90

G1615-16

G1615-30

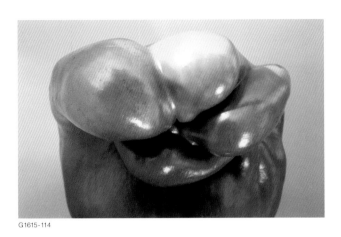

G1615-114

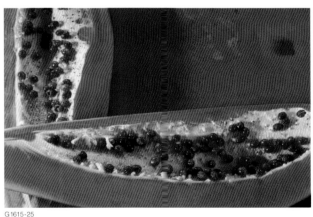

G1615-173

G1615-188

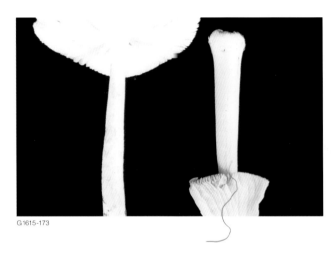

G1615-25

G1615-44

G1615-23

G1616-31

G1616-33

G1616-30

G1616-37

G1616-08

G1616-34

G1616-27

G1616-14

G1617-26

G1617-34

G1617-22

G1617-05

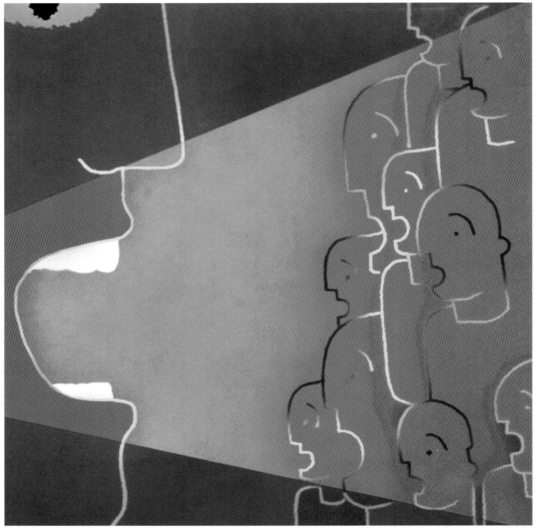

G1621-17

G1621-40

G1621-43

G1621-51

G1621-10

G1621-12

G1621-58

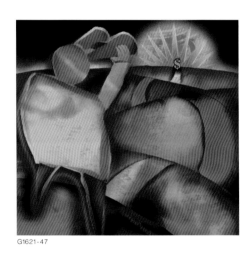

G1621-47

G1621-36

G1621-35

G1621-53

G1623-21

G1623-29

G1623-02

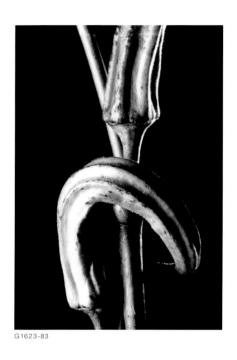

G1623-83

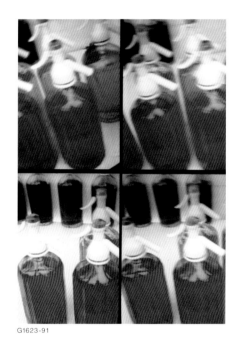

G1623-91

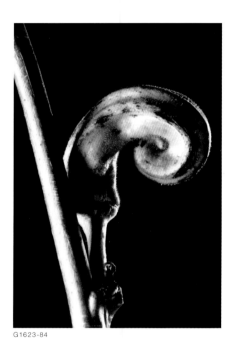

G1623-84

G1623-71

G1623-90

G1623-106

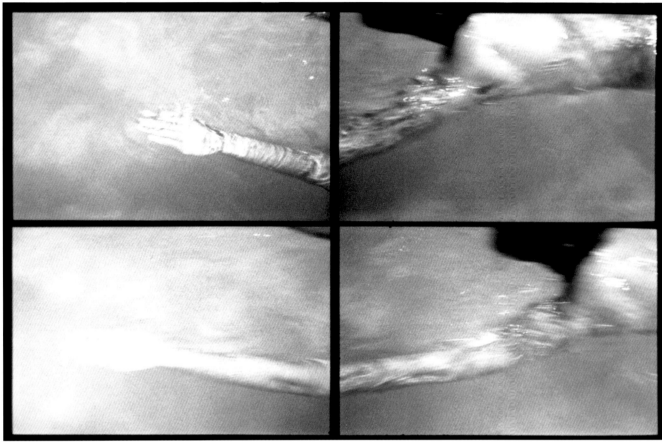

G1623-50

G1623-04

G1618-07

G1618-10

G1618-08

G1618-03

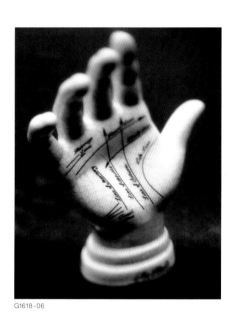

G1618-06

G1618-05

G1618-02

G1618-09

G1618-04

G1618-01

G1624-34

G1624-03

G1624-14

G1624-18

G1624-45

G1624-46

G1624-58

G1624-50

G1625-78

G1625-75

G1628-70

G1628-52

G1628-72

G1628-57

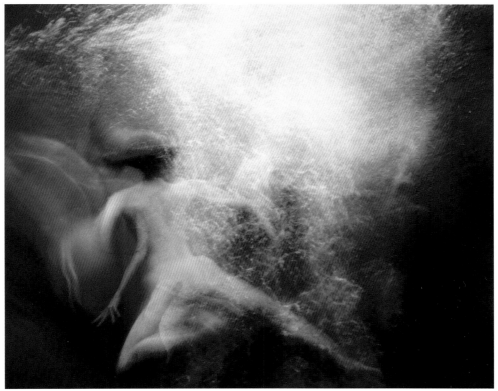

G1628-73

G1628-49

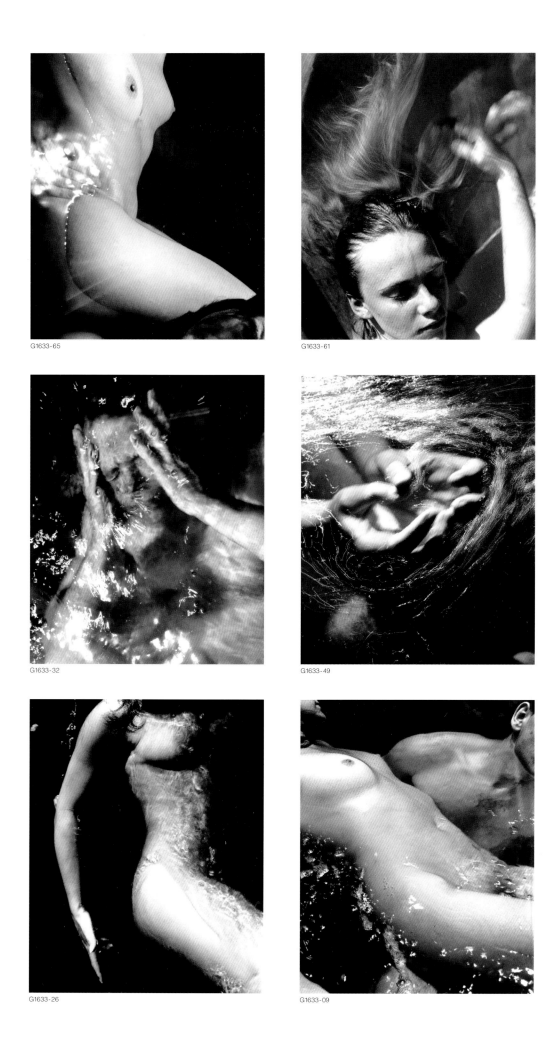

G1633-65

G1633-61

G1633-32

G1633-49

G1633-26

G1633-09

G1633-77

G1633-76

G1611-01

G1611-07

G1611-04

G1611-10

G1611-05

G1611-06

G1611-02

G1611-09

G1611-03

G1611-08

G1632-83

G1632-82

G1632-80

G1632-121

G1632-74

G1632-77

G1632-87

G1632-79

G1632-81

G1632-48

G1632-161

G1632-195

G1632-160

G1632-106

G1632-151

G1630-126

G1630-152

G1630-145

G1630-130

G1630-19

G1630-59

G1630-78

G1630-13

G1630-11

G1630-61

G1630-88

G1631-531

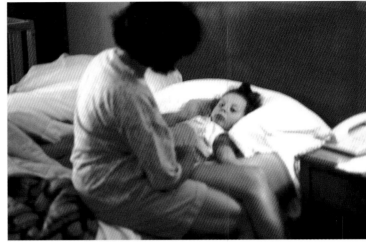

G1631-534

G1631-533

G1631-530

G1631-528

G1631-529

G1631-285

G1631-532

G1631-236

G1631-155

G1631-297

G1631-463

G1636-36

G1636-35

G1636-38

G1636-16

G1636-47

G1638-16

G1638-02

G1638-29

G1638-10

G1638-36

G1638-06

G1638-09

G1638-04

G1638-28

G1638-27

G1638-24

G1638-20

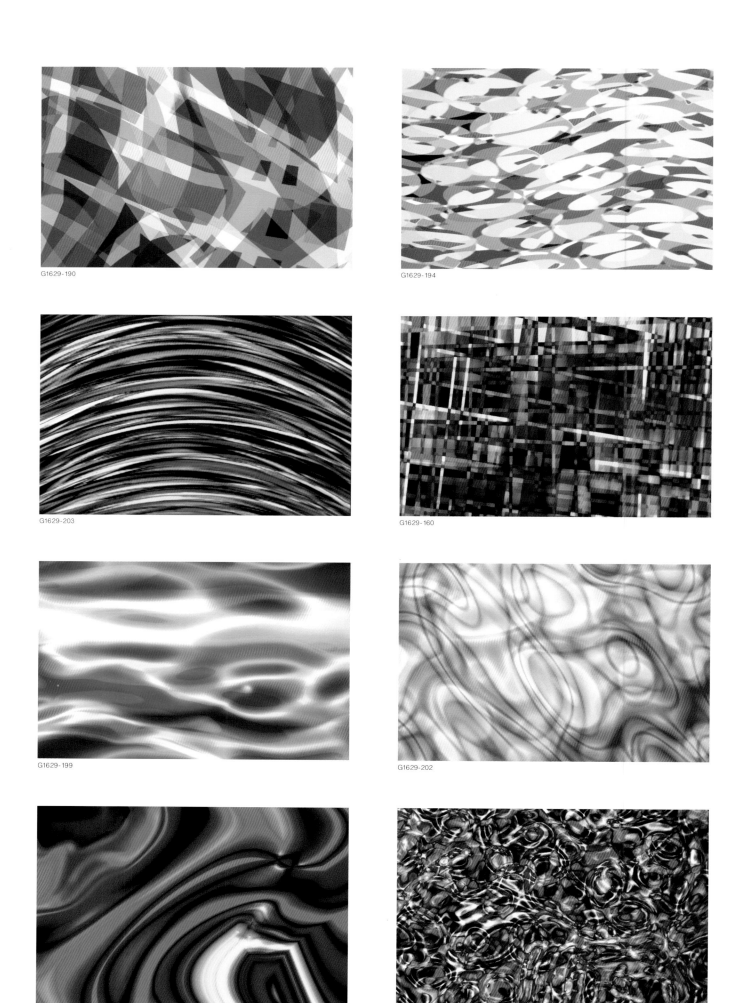

G1629-190

G1629-194

G1629-203

G1629-160

G1629-199

G1629-202

G1629-01

G1629-34

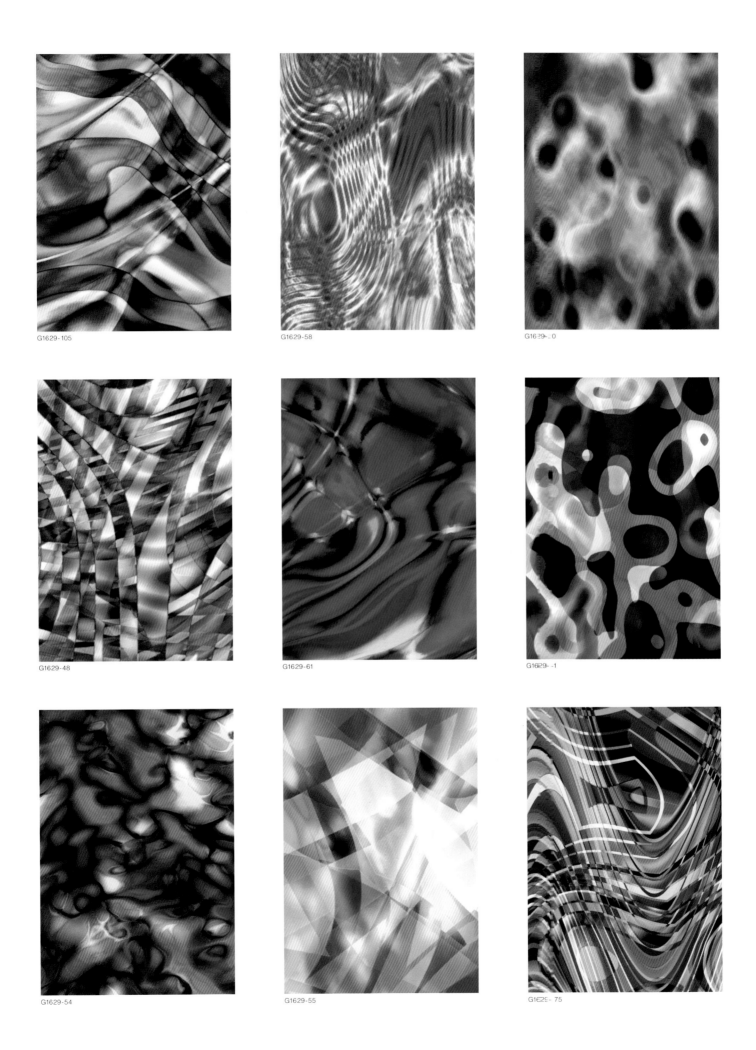

G1629-105

G1629-58

G1629-10

G1629-48

G1629-61

G1629-1

G1629-54

G1629-55

G1629-75

G1639-1153

G1639-1148

G1639-1152

G1639-1154

G1639-1155

G1639-1150

G1639-1151

G1639-1149

G1640-449

G1640-262

G1640-447

G1640-448

G1640-446

G1640-109

G1640-445

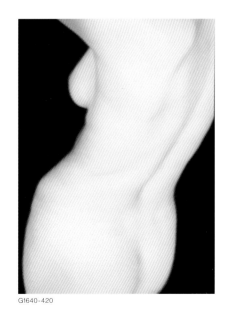

G1640-420

G1640-450

G1640-317

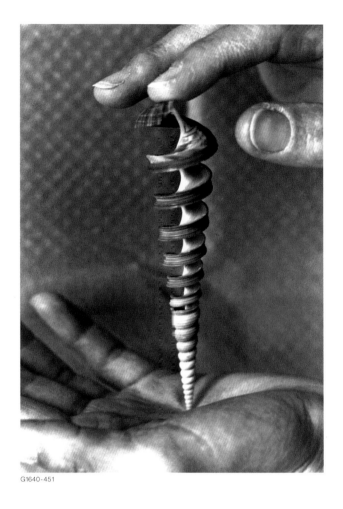

G1640-451

G1640-453

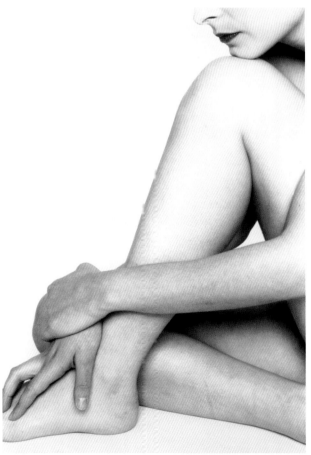

G1640-452

G1643-65

G1643-51

G1643-48

G1643-50

G1643-66

G1643-23

G1643-31

G1643-53

G1643-09

G1643-11

G1643-01

G1643-22

G1644-52

G1644-35

G1644-28

G1644-24

G1644-03

G1644-63

G1644-25

G1644-34

G1644-22

G1644-04

G1644-05

G1644-65

G1645-69

G1645-70

G1645-24

G1645-53

G1645-63

G1645-45

G1645-64

G1646-23

G1646-22

G1646-08

G1646-19

G1647-103

G1647-186

G1647-61

G1647-54

G1647-91

G1649-379

G1649-47

G1649-22

G1649-195

G1649-100

G1649-292

G1649-10

G1649-129

G1649-254

G1649-377

G1649-276

G1649-261

G1649-248

G1649-265

G1649-246

G1649-284

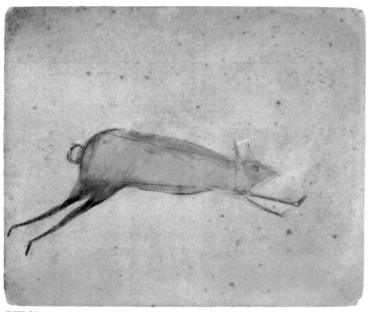

G1622-34

G1622-17

G1622-35

G1622-36

G1622-27

G1622-23

G1622-19

G1622-38

G1622-28

G1622-66

G1651-04

G1651-03

G1651-07

G1651-12

G1651-05

G1651-01

G1651-06

G1651-10

G1651-08

G1651-02

G1651-11

G1651-09

G1652-28

G1652-24

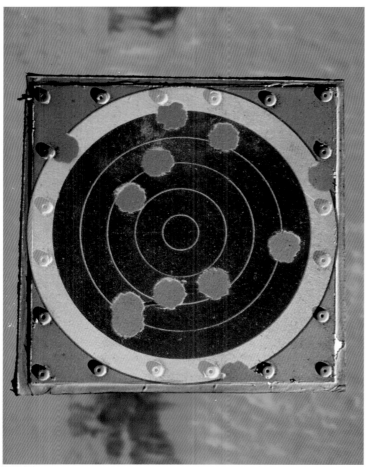

G1652-29

G1652-34

G1652-11

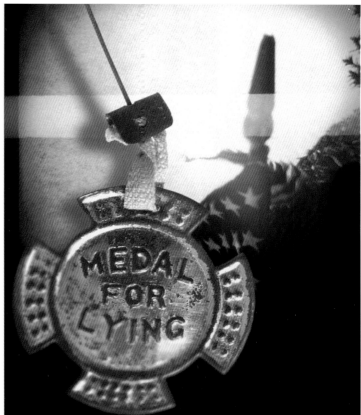

G1652-35

G1652-09

G1652-10

G1661-87

G1661-85

G1661-81

G1661-88

G1661-39

G1661-14

G1661-05

G1653-86

G1653-79

G1653-78

G1653-77

G1653-82

G1653-80

G1653-10

G1653-81

G1653-57

G1653-56

G1653-85

81655-242

81655-231

81655-231

81655-16

81655-09

81655-155

81655-35

81655-143

81655-95

81655-20

81655-192

81655-190

G1659-70

G1659-56

G1659-58

G1659-59

G1659-37

G1659-61

G1659-65

G1659-68

G1659-64

G1659-60

G1659-57

G1659-67

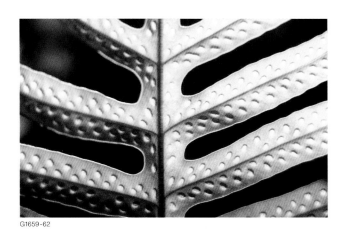

G1659-62

G1659-69

G1659-66

G1659-29

G1659-63

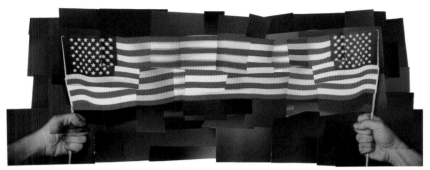

G1654-37

G1654-06

G1654-07

G1654-11

G1654-44

G1654-08

G1654-29

G1662-0

G1662-02

G1662-05

G1662-0

G1662-08

G1662-10

G1662-0

G1662-03

G1662-01

G1662-09

INDEX TO
PHOTOGRAPHERS

PHOTOGRAPHERS

PHOTOGRAPHERS

INDEX TO SUBJECTS

SUBJECTS

SUBJECTS

SUBJECTS

S U B J E C T S

SUBJECTS

SUBJECTS

NOTES

NOTES